GUNS AND CARRIAGES

GUNS AND CARRIAGES

THE CONSTRUCTION OF THE WORLD'S FIRST REPRODUCTION MONCRIEFF DEPRESSION MOUNTING

AUSTIN C. CARPENTER FSA

HALSGROVE

First published in Great Britain in 1999

Copyright © 1998 Austin C. Carpenter

British Library Cataloguing-in-Publication Data
A CIP record for this title is available from the British Library

ISBN 1 84114 027 9

HALSGROVE
Publishing, Media and Distribution

Halsgrove House
Lower Moor Way
Tiverton, Devon EX16 6SS
Tel: 01884 243242
Fax: 01884 243325

The jacket illustrations: front cover main image – elevation of the Moncrieff carriage with 110-pounder Armstrong gun being fired at Crownhill Fort, Plymouth. Inset left: loading Blomefield gun on a blocked up traversing carriage. Inset right: Full elevation of Moncrieff carriage and gun, with author. Back cover: Volunteer gun detachment hauling the Moncrieff carriage down for loading.

Printed and bound in Great Britain by WBC, Bridgend.

CONTENTS

The author with the reproduction Moncrieff carriage and gun built under his guidance and supervision in 1998 at Crownhill Fort, Plymouth.

ACKNOWLEDGEMENTS

The following have all, at sometime, contributed in some small way to the presentation of Crownhill Fort, Plymouth, as the public see it today, regarding its present armaments: James Breslin, Paul Roberts, Tom Hitchins, Norman Allen, Geoffrey Westlake, Lewis Bate, John Symons, Shaun McCoy, Margaret Worth, David Martin, Jonathan Tricker, Irons Bros Limited, Scot Milne, Nigel Burt, Cash-Lifts Cranes, Duncan Williams, David Moore, Stephen Collinson, Andrew Watts, Nigel Chapman. Also the foundry operators at Irons Bros Foundry, Cornwall. Debbie Hamilton typed the manuscript which is sincerely appreciated.

'Infantry and Gunners Exercising' Pendennis Castle, Falmouth, Cornwall. A watercolour in the author's collection, painted in the manner of Paul Sandby c. 1800.

INTRODUCTION

The early nineteen sixties saw the introduction of the organisation known today as the Sealed Knot. Its aims were to promote and re-enact the life and times of the English Civil War, 1649-1660, with military demonstrations taking place at various sites known to have been the actual location where Civil War battles took place.

The activities of the Sealed Knot and similar organisations exemplifies the growing interest in English military history and has led to considerable advances in the study and reproduction of muskets, pistols, uniforms and equipment, guns and carriages. This in turn has helped to enhance historic fortifications and to preserve what original cannon are still to be found in these islands.

The coastal defences in the West Country covering such historic sites as Portland Castle, Dartmouth Castle, Drake's Island, St Mawes Castle, Pendennis Castle and the fortifications of the Isles of Scilly, are only now becoming, in relation to their original armament, anything like they were at the time of the Napoleonic Wars.

The Citadel, Plymouth, mounted twenty-six pieces of ordnance, the Garrison at St Mary's, Isles of Scilly, over eighteen guns and carriages, and by 1865-1880, Crownhill Fort could display at least twenty pieces, with such examples as 7-inch rifled breech-loaders of Armstrong First Principal, designed and accepted by the then War Department (shortly followed by rejection by the Navy), but which continued to be retained by the Army and the colonies. This class of gun can be seen today on the casemate carriage and the Moncrieff carriage at Crownhill Fort, Plymouth.

Austin C. Carpenter
Ivybridge, Devon

The gatehouse at Crownhill Fort, Plymouth.

PART ONE
CROWNHILL FORT

The Landmark Trust, the present owners of Crownhill Fort, acquired it by purchase in 1986. Lying six miles north-east of the city centre, it is one of a group of Palmerston Fortifications which still encircle the north-west and eastern perimeter of Plymouth.

Crownhill Fort, in the eyes of the old Ancient Monuments division of the Department of the Environment, was always considered to be the best preserved of the Victorian Palmerston Fortifications. From the author's experience in that organisation, a careful watch was kept as to its future should it ever come on the market. It had already been scheduled as an Ancient Monument.

Since taking up his post, Paul Roberts, Site Manager for the Landmark Trust had, on numerous occasions, approached the author with regard to the re-arming of the Fort with original pieces, or reproduction guns, in order to enhance the fort and to give the visiting public a feel of what the heavy ordnance of this period would have looked like.

Having, from considerable experience in this field, known what would be involved in the production of large reproduction period guns and their carriages, and well aware of the cost involved, I was somewhat unenthusiastic that this project would every materialise.

How wrong I was! By January 1997 the design of carriages and research into the availability and procurement of genuine period cannon was under way.

More than thirty years associated with castles, forts and historic houses had already given me a good background to period gun emplacements, and I knew what type of carriages and guns the Crownhill site would have displayed between the 1860s–1880s. From the hundreds of guns I had recorded around the world, and from knowledge of their availability, I also knew that obtaining genuine period pieces of the type installed in Crownhill Fort was to be very difficult.

Having carried out a survey of all period cannon registered with the Tower of London Armouries, along with those in the care of English Heritage, in the 1980s, I knew of a number of available pieces. Some had been uprighted as bollards for the mooring of ships, and could possibly be retrieved from their static role, while others had been inverted into the ground in order to protect the corners and structures of buildings.

The first two which came to mind were cast-iron 32-pounder smooth bore cannon of George III period (1760-1820), which had been removed by the military (against my advice) from the end of the drawbridge, which they were to protect, at the approach to Tregantle Fort in East Cornwall. These had now been deposited adjacent to the keep within that fort. These two guns, one being cast by the Carron Ironworks at Falkirk, Scotland, and dated 1811, and the other piece cast by Walker and Company of Rotherham, Yorkshire, of an approximate date of 1814, were in good shootable condition with all their original markings and weight etc. alongside the royal cypher.

Neither the military nor the Department of the Environment took any action to display these two guns by having carriages built, which was their original intention, so the pieces lay at Tregantle until noticed by Major Thomas Hitchins (Retd), who approached the military to try to secure these historic cannon. This was eventually agreed and they were transferred to Crownhill Fort where they were shot-blasted and painted and placed on wooden blocks within the two Haxo casements.

DECISION TO DISPLAY FOUR CLASSES OF PERIOD ORDNANCE

The existence of documentary evidence dating from the mid-nineteenth century, and covering the various types of guns and carriages, was an asset in making a decision as to what, and how many pieces, should in the first instance be displayed at Crownhill.

A contract, drawn up by Paul Roberts, stipulated that the following would be required:

One Moncrieff depression gun and carriage Mark II to take a 110-pounder RBL of 82 cwt reproduction. (Plate 1).

One blocked-up-traversing siege carriage (wood) to take one of the 32 pounder SB guns from Tregantle Fort. (Plate 2).

One casemate carriage (wood) to take a reproduction 110 pounder RBL of 82 cwt. (Plate 3).

Four iron carriages and slides to take 32 pounder SBBL converted guns for flank and caponier emplacements (guns to be reproduction). (Plate 4).

Plate 1: *Completed new Moncrieff carriage with Armstrong 110-pounder breech loading gun in its emplacement.*

CROWNHILL FORT - PLYMOUTH

PLAN SHOWING LOCATION OF ORIGINAL AND REPRODUCTION ORDNANCE

IT WAS RECORDED IN 1893 THAT THE FULL
COMPLEMENT OF ARMAMENT MOUNTED AT
CROWNHILL WAS AS FOLLOWS:
SEVEN 64-POUNDER RML
ELEVEN 7-INCH RBL
FOURTEEN 32-POUNDER SBBL
SIX 25-POUNDER RML

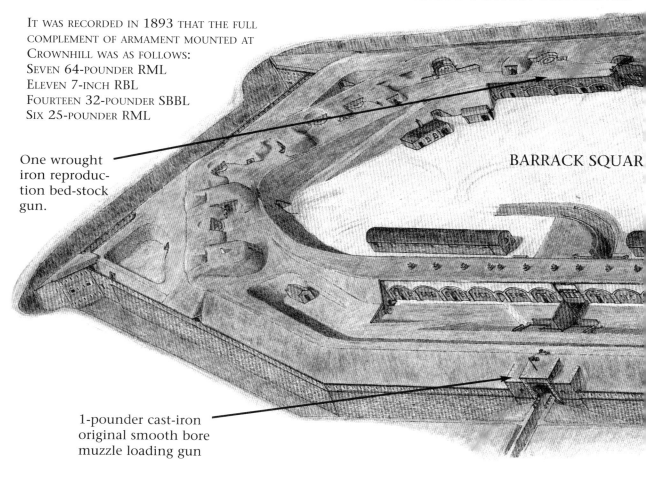

One wrought
iron reproduc-
tion bed-stock
gun.

BARRACK SQUAR

1-pounder cast-iron
original smooth bore
muzzle loading gun

GUNS AND CARRIAGES

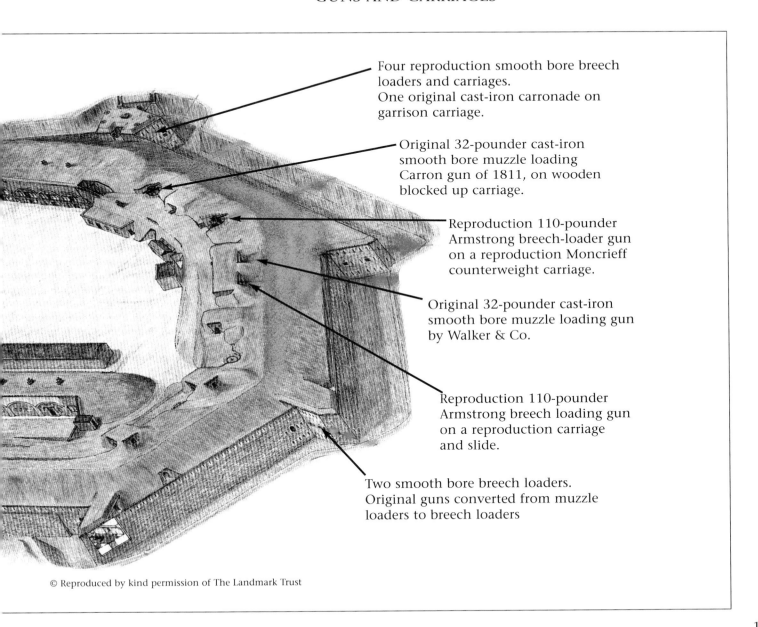

Four reproduction smooth bore breech loaders and carriages.
One original cast-iron carronade on garrison carriage.

Original 32-pounder cast-iron smooth bore muzzle loading Carron gun of 1811, on wooden blocked up carriage.

Reproduction 110-pounder Armstrong breech-loader gun on a reproduction Moncrieff counterweight carriage.

Original 32-pounder cast-iron smooth bore muzzle loading gun by Walker & Co.

Reproduction 110-pounder Armstrong breech loading gun on a reproduction carriage and slide.

Two smooth bore breech loaders. Original guns converted from muzzle loaders to breech loaders

Plate 2: *Blocked-up carriage and gun in its C pivot emplacement. A 32-pounder muzzle loading gun of 1811.*

Plate 3: *Casemate carriage and gun in its Haxo casemate. Gun 7-inch breech loader.*

Plate 4: *Caponier guns in their final position showing brass breech carrier mechanism.*

PART TWO

MAKING THE GUNS

As consultant to the Landmark Trust for this project, models and designs of the various requirements were exhibited. These were then used, along with drawings, to obtain quotations for their manufacture.

From past experience in the building of military gun carriages I have found the choice of timbers can be difficult. We were only too aware that English timbers such as oak, ash, elm and pitch pine were regularly specified by the Board of Ordnance and the War Department. In earlier days these were easy to obtain in large quantities and, most important, 80% dry with a moisture content down to 18–20%. To obtain large English timbers in 6-inch plank, 24-inches wide, and dry, is more or less impossible today, so timbers from abroad were looked at.

Hardwoods such as iroko, sabicu, utile and opepi had also been included in the old War Department schedule and imported into England for the military, and I decided from past experience to use West African Iroko. It is a timber which need not be fully seasoned before use.

The metal carriages were to be made of steel. To obtain wrought iron in very large sections, as originally used, was out of the question.

For the reproduction guns, i.e. the 1860–80 RBLs and the SBBLs, grade 18 cast-iron was specified, with the bore of both types being fitted with a cold-drawn seamless steel tube and threaded breech chamber. Molten cast-iron was to be run around these bore liners to form the outside casing and contour of each piece.

The Cornish firm of Irons Bros of Wadebridge undertook to quote for the relevant carriages. The choice of this company meant that foundry work, machinery, engineering and woodwork could take place within the same complex, and with their previous experience in the casting of cannon for English Heritage and the Tower of London sites, they were well aware of the pitfalls and difficulties encountered in the production of such pieces.

Initially difficulties were encountered in obtaining West African iroko in such sizes as 16 feet x 12

Plate 5: *There was a delay of three months in obtaining the timber in large sizes from West Africa.*

Plate 6: *Two halves of the wooden gun pattern fabricated by Lewis Bate, the foundry pattern maker.*

Plate 7: *The wooden stave built pattern to make the Armstrong guns being turned in a large lathe.*

inches x 12 inches, and 6 feet x 24 inches x 6 inches **(Plate 5)**. Thus we were delayed at the outset by something like three months, and were forced to proceed with the various component manufacture such as casting in bronze and machining in steel of bore-liners, breech carriers, breech blocks, etc. for the 32-pounder SBBLs. Meanwhile pattern-maker, Lewis Bate, fabricated

in timber the pattern for the 7-inch 110-pounder breech loading gun **(Plate 6)**.

Massive lathes were then used to machine the patterns from which the foundry could cast the guns as and when required, one for the Casemate slide and one for the Moncrieff depression carriage **(Plate 7)**.

Plate 8: A C pivot mounting with its centre pivot of cast iron and its circular racer of wrought iron to take the blocked-up carriage.

Plate 9: *Moncrieff gun emplacement, the centre iron pintle has a bronze bush which is marked MONCRIEFF MK II, also traversing sweep-plates. Shell and cartridge stores are to right and left. Approximate date 1875.*

At this time, early in 1997, a survey was made of each relevant emplacements at Crownhill Fort **(Plates 8 and 9)**. Their floor areas and their individual racers (traversing rails) were marked out on the workshop floor **(Plate 10)**, so that each carriage could be built as though constructed in their individual emplacements on site. Also at this time a start was made on the Moncrieff carriage,

with Norman Allen, the engineer I specifically chose to undertake this, working under my direct supervision.

Dimensions for the Mark II Moncrieff carriage were taken from original plans and elevations in the War Department Handbooks for 1885 and 1897 **(Plate 11)**. These also covered the dimen-

Plate 15: *Blocked-up carriage and slide under construction to be eventually set up on the C pivot emplacement.*

April 1997 saw the start of the blocked-up wooden traversing siege carriage for the C pivot emplacement (**Plate 15**) to take the cast-iron 32-pounder smooth bored gun of Blomefield type, dated 1811 'Carron'; the emplacement racers (rails) being set out on large plywood sheets so that the whole of the carriage and slide could be built up as if on site, and able to traverse its 360°. At around this time machining of the SBBLs (smooth bore breech-loaders) breech-blocks were in hand, these guns and carriages being destined for the caponier at the fort and to be four in number.

By 31 July 1997 the position regarding the manufacture of the casemate carriage and slide was under consideration and construction was put in hand (**Plate 16**). West African Iroko was also

Plate 16: *New casemate carriage and slide under construction for the Haxo casemate.*

chosen as the timber for this carriage which was of basically the same construction as the blocked up type. However, the casemate carriage and slide was constructed low to the floor to enable the gun to fire through a gun port, as opposed to its counterpart, the blocked-up type, which is elevated to fire over a 6-foot parapet, its gun detachment being under cover at all times.

Plate 17: *Hauling the original 32 pounder Blomefield gun to the C pivot site for the mounting of the piece.*

The effort of moving one of the 32-pounder 58 cwt smooth bore guns, the piece dated 1811, was put in hand in early July. Its passage along the ramparts to its C pivot site went smoothly and was now ready for its blocked-up carriage when it arrived (**Plate 17**).

The first casting of the Armstrong 110-pounder took place on 16 September following the preparation of the large steel mould-box (**Plate 18**). The twin sections of the wooden pattern for the gun were positioned in the mould and carefully packed around with moulding sand. With the

Plate 18: *Heating the sand-mould in which the gun will be cast for a new 110-pounder breech loader.*

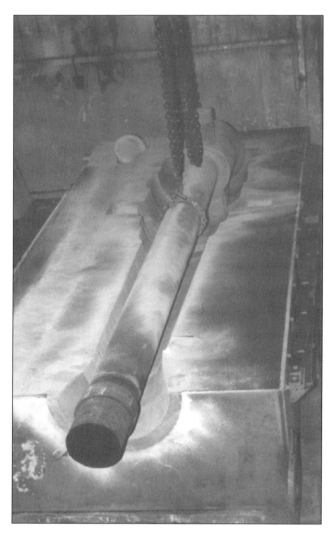

Plate 19: *Moulding box and bore-liner in position, prior to closing the mould when the whole box will be uprighted and the molten iron poured.*

Plate 20: *New Armstrong gun after removal from its mould, showing the feeder and risers, awaiting fettling.*

wooden pattern removed, the shape of the gun is visible and the steel bore liner is placed within the mould (**Plate 19**). The two halves of the mould box are then closed.

The skill of the foundry moulders determines the final outcome of the product, any casting is only as good as the pattern, the moulders and the running of the molten iron. The melting point of cast-iron is 1100°C, the pouring temperature is 1260°C. Great skill and effort go into the casting

of large complicated shapes, but there is no guarantee that the casting will be successful. The cost of failure in the case of the Armstrong gun cast would have been in the region of £7000–£8000.

A gun with the weight of say, four tons, would require at least 5–6 days to cool in its mould. To accelerate the cooling time is courting trouble, encouraging fast shrinking and fractures. On the removal of the casting from its moulding box (**Plate 20**) it then needs to be fettled, a process of

Plate 21: *7-inch 110-pounder reproduction breech-loader of 1861 Armstrong gun of cast-iron with smooth bore liner in steel.*

cutting off all excrescences and feeding runners of iron, to achieve a clean gun which can now have its breech mechanism fitted (**Plate 21**).

On 29 July 1997 we saw the delivery of the wooden blocked-up carriage to Crownhill Fort, Plymouth. Sixteen days later the lifting equipment in the form of a mobile crane arrived to lift the wooden carriage and platform. These were transported up one of the ramps to their perma-nent site and lowered on to a circular rail and cen-tre pivot. The 1811 cannon could now also be lifted and settled on to its carriage, supported by its trunnions, and was coupled to its rear the ele-vating screw, which gives the piece its elevation and depression (**Plate 22**).

On 29 October 1997 the casemate carriage plat-form and gun were delivered to Crownhill Fort and a team, headed by the author and John

Plate 22: *Cast-iron original 1811 Blomefield gun being lowered on to its new blocked-up wooden carriage and slide on it C pivot mounting.*

Symons, were on hand to unload and install the whole assembly into its casemate at the north east elevation of the ramparts. The unloading of the various units was helped by the transport vehicle, a 'Hyab' type crane, which was able to run a certain distance up the ramp and assist with the lifting off and placing of gun, carriage and slide at the entrance to the casemate (**Plates 23/24**).

Plate 23 (opposite): *Casemate carriage and slide about to enter its Haxo emplacement, and to be set upon its traversing rail.*

Plate 24 (above): *New Armstrong gun of 82 cwt being unloaded for the 'Haxo' casemate.*

Plate 25: *Casemate carriage and gun being fired by John Symons and his detachment for the first time.*

GUNS AND CARRIAGES

Within two days the piece and its carriage were installed and the recently formed gun detachment were now able to start training in earnest to load, train and traverse the gun and carriage, all as laid down the original training manual of the 1880s (**Plate 25**).

Progress continued to be made on the construction of the Moncrieff depression carriage to a stage where the main carriage frames, on which the gun is supported, could be raised or lowered by the effort of turning the capstan heads with handspikes (levers) and controlled by the friction handbrake.

By this time the details for the making of the elevating rack, gears and hand-wheel were to hand, and work progressed towards the aim of being able to elevate the gun's muzzle from the horizontal to 15°, and to depress it by 4°, even while the piece is in its raised position above the emplacement's parapet.

At this stage of the Moncrieff construction it was time to give consideration to the casting of the second 110 pounder breech loading gun. The bore liner and threaded breech were being worked upon and by the 20 November they were ready to go to the foundry for incorporation into the moulding of this second piece.

On Thursday, 27 November the second gun was cast. The moulding box was opened four days later and from a general inspection it appeared to be a successful casting. Fettling was to follow.

On a visit to the foundry on 11 December it was noted that the second gun had been fettled and progress was being made with the fitting of breech-block, breech screw, tappet ring and lever etc., while at the same time the final adjustment to the Moncrieff's elevating worm and rack were in hand (**Plates 26, 27 and 28**).

At this time further progress was made on components for the SBBLs (smooth bore breech-loading guns). For the four guns required for the caponier at the north elevation of the fort, the pattern maker produced patterns for the trunnion bearings, flanges to take the trucks (front and rear), and a full size wooden pattern of the 32-pounder breech-loading gun to be cast in cast-iron (**Plate 29**). This latter gun was to be an exact copy of the original fourteen which were converted to breech-loaders in the early 1880s, and which were at the fort at that time for flank defence and the training of gun detachments. In this configuration they would be loaded to fire canister shot, in effect extremely large shotguns.

The carriage components for these pieces were cast in spheroidal graphite, a material as strong as steel. The carriage cheeks were made in mild steel with riveted angle iron supports (**Plate 30**).

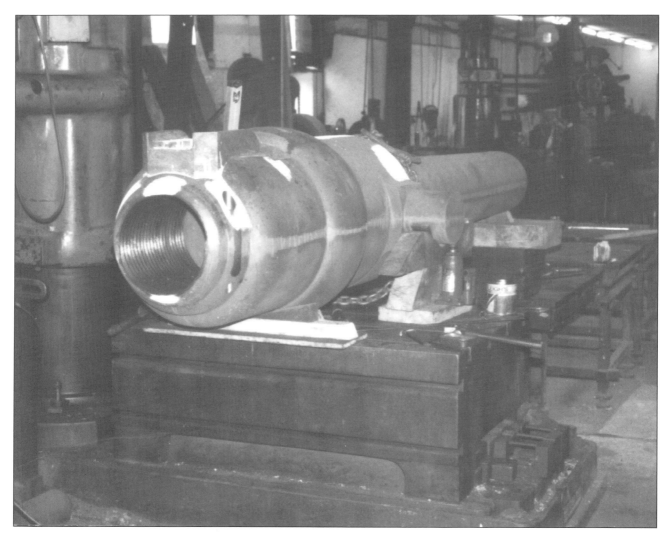

Plate 26: *New Armstrong gun after having its breech screw machined in the boring mill at the Wadebridge foundry.*

Plate 27: *Breech block and tappet ring for the new 110-pounder Armstrong guns, await machining.*

Plate 28: *Breech-screw tappet ring and lever for the new 110 pounder guns.*

GUNS AND CARRIAGES

By the 19 December the Moncrieff elevator rack and control arms were completed. The lower half of the wooden pattern of the gun was set upon the elevators, in what would be the guns mounted position, in order to test the elevating and running down of the elevators. This was proved to work satisfactorily and could be worked by two men using hand spikes (**Plates 31 and 32**).

Early January 1998 saw the fitting of the bronze bearings for the elevator trunnion holes to take the 110-pounder gun and the cap squares were fabricated and fitted.

The dismantling of the main elevator cheeks (in hand with the cutting out of four 3/8 inch steel cheeks, which were to be riveted to each outside and inner face of the cast-iron core cheeks), the four counter-balance weights (in all totalling an approximate weight of 5.5 tons) each required wooden patterns so they could be cast in cast-iron. By the 24 January the four wooden patterns were made and sent to the foundry for moulding and casting. Also at this time the casting of small components in S.G. iron for the SBBLs was in hand.

On my visit to the foundry on 23 January, the marking out and drilling for riveting of the inner and outer cheek plates to the elevator frames was to commence. The first of the four 32-pounder cast-iron breech loaders for the caponier at Crownhill Fort was to be cast by the end of January, while the machining of the breech components for the guns was already in hand.

By this time the 7-inch breech-loading gun for the Moncrieff carriage had its breech mechanism fitted and working and awaiting painting.

Friday 30 January saw the setting up of the two cast-iron elevators along with two of the 3/8 inch side cheek plates for drilling to take the 300 or so rivets. The completion of the drilling and the fixing of the red-hot rivets was completed by the 13 February, at the same time as the making up of the four bronze breech-block carriers for the SBBLs with their internal mechanism.

The first of the 32-pounder SBBLs was cast and the second of these guns was poured by the 13 February (**Plate 33**).

At this time the four counter-balance weights were being cast for the elevator of the Moncrieff carriage.

On the following Wednesday the carriage and elevator, along with the first of the RBLs, was taken to the main workshop where an overhead gantry-lift would assist in the assembly of elevator and gun. This was completed by the 13 February and was, in fact, erected and working with the aid of the gantry to operate the rise and fall of the gun

Plate 29: *Full size wooden pattern by Lewis Bate for the 32 pounder Caponier guns.*

Plate 30: *Awaiting painting, the carriage and slide for the Caponier guns, made in mild steel and spheroidal graphite, a high quality cast steel.*

Plate 31: *Platform with elevator frame and half-section of the wooden gun pattern set up to test the rise and fall of the elevator. The gun is shown in the elevated position.*

Plate 32: *The elevator and wooden gun pattern in the recoiled position, operated by the elevator rack and control arms.*

Plate 33: *The 32-pounder cast-iron gun, removed from the mould after casting, awaiting the cutting off of the riser.*

Plate 34: *The Moncrieff counter-balance weight and the elevators, showing the eleven holes by which it is secured by bolts to the base of the elevator.*

and elevator. At about this time the iron carriages for the four SBBLs were in hand with the fabrication of the main beds and all their fittings.

With the counter-balance weights being cast, they were set up for the boring of the 11 x 11/2-inch holes. These would take the heavy bolts which pass through the front of the elevator and carry the counter balance weights (**Plate 34**).

By the 17 February completion of the boring of the counter-weight was complete and the full assembly of the Moncrieff was under way. On the 18 February the test runs of elevation and depression of the gun and carriage were being tested and it was found that three men, one man on the brake lever and two on the capstans handspikes, could elevate and depress the carriage and gun.

Teething troubles were found and eased, oils and grease applied to all frictional areas, which greatly assisted the running up and down of gun and carriage.

Dry runs were demonstrated to James Breslin (Landmark Trust) and Win Scutt (Plymouth City Museum) who visited the foundry. The whole Moncrieff assembly could now be painted and dismantled for the transportation to Crownhill Fort on the 24 February for site installation.

Monday 23 February saw the delivery of the main Moncrieff platform and counter-weight to Crownhill Fort, with the delivery on the following day of the elevator and the large breech loading gun (**Plates 35, 36 and 37**).

The assembly took place over three days with large cranes and lifting equipment supplied by the Plymouth firm Cashlifts, with the final installation of the 5.5 ton counter-weights, bolted in position by Norman Allen and Nigel Chapman. The running up and down of the gun and elevator could then be practised (**Plate 38**).

Plate 35: *Westcountry cranes lifting in the 5 ton counter-balance weight to its emplacement.*

Wednesday 25 February, saw the firing of all three guns. First the original Blomefield gun on the wooden blocked up carriage and slide (**Plate 39**), then the reproduction casemate RBL gun on its wooden casemate slide, and finally the Moncrieff.

Plate 36: *The elevator which carries the gun on the Moncrieff carriage being lowered near its emplacement.*

Plate 37: *The platform of the Moncrieff carriage which takes the elevator.*

Plate 38: *The team which set up the Moncrieff gun and carriage toasting the effort. From left to right: Four men from Cash-Lifts, Margaret Worth, the author, Norman Allen, Nigel Chapman, John Symons and James Breslin.*

Plate 39: *32-pounder of 1811 being fired from its blocked-up carriage and slide.*

GUNS AND CARRIAGES

With full photographs and television coverage, the Plymouth Artillery Volunteers, newly formed under their Commander John Symons, loaded all three guns and fired the first two. The privilege of the first firing of the Moncrieff was given to the author. All the guns fired without any hesitation and with considerable noise. All that now remained was the supervision of the completion of the manufacture of the four SBBLs which were to be set up in the caponier.

A visit to the foundry on 2 March saw the near completion of the first SBBL carriage and the casting of No. 3 BL cast-iron gun (**Plate 40**).

The first of these three guns was set up in the boring mill and had its brass breech-carrier fitted.

Plate 41: *New breech-blocks being fitted to cast-iron caponier guns, in the boring mill at the foundry.*

(**Plate 41**). This carrier takes the breech-block and allows it to slide into the breech chamber. By 11 March the first of the four SBBLs carriages was completed, and work could now proceed to produce the remaining three carriages by copying the first completed example.

By 30 March all four SBBLs were completed with the final assembly of their four carriages, involving the use of red-hot rivets through all the main frame members of the steel cheeks.

A site visit to the foundry on 2 April 1998 saw the final riveting of the main steel carriage cheeks, and with the guns and breech blocks now complete, the guns and their carriages were given their final coat of paint.

Plate 40: *Gun and carriage with its slide in the process of manufacture and nearing completion.*

Plate 42: *Four reproduction cast-iron 32 pounder breech-loading smooth-bored guns on the new iron carriages for the north caponier Crownhill Fort.*

The four guns and carriages were delivered to Crownhill Fort on 14 April 1998 and displayed on the barrack square (**Plate 42**).

The installation in the caponier of these pieces was now the responsibility of the Landmark Trust Management, and within a few days the four pieces were set up in the main caponier. My own involvement as consultant for the production of the six guns and seven carriages and their delivery to Crownhill was over. Throughout the succeeding summers the guns of Crownhill Fort are fired at specific intervals for the visiting public, who are able to watch the local volunteers, 2nd Battery, 7th Western Brigade, Royal Garrison Artillery, going through all drills and procedures to work and fire the various types of heavy guns set up in this fort (**Plate 43**).

Plate 43: *Gun detachment with the reproduction Armstrong gun on its casemate carriage and slide within the Haxo casemate. From left to right: John Symons, Christopher Bailey, Richard Eva, James Breslin, Colin Wetton and Michael Davis.*

Plate 44: *The Moncrieff gun and carriage in the raised firing position within the emplacement over-looking the north-east ditch.*

PART THREE
ALEXANDER MONCRIEFF 1829-1906

Born in Edinburgh, Alexander Moncrieff made a study of civil engineering, but did not continue with it. Instead, on 16 April 1855, he was commissioned into the Forfar and Kincardine Artillery (Militia), and he spent some time in the Crimea, witnessing the Russian guns being disabled in the Mamelon Fort in June 1855.

From this experience he returned to England and set about designing a disappearing artillery carriage. His idea and design was to store the thrust of the recoil so that it could be used to raise the gun to the firing position over the lip of its parapet after reloading. The emplacement thus served to protect the gun detachment whilst engaged in loading.

Moncrieff transferred to the Edinburgh Artillery Militia in 1863, becoming a major in 1872, whilst working on the design and supervision of his disappearing carriages at Woolwich Arsenal. Promoted to colonel in 1878 and elected a Fellow of the Royal Society in 1871. He was knighted in 1890 (**Plates 44, 45, 46 and 47**).

Plate 45: *The Moncrieff gun and carriage in the depressed position for loading with the model made by the author. The gun and carriage lie below the 9 foot parapet.*

GUNS AND CARRIAGES

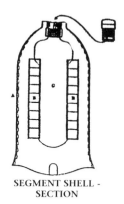

SEGMENT SHELL - SECTION

SOLID SHOT

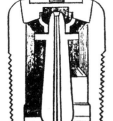

PILLAR PERCUSSION FUSE - SECTION

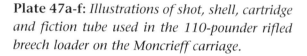

Plate 46: *The Moncrieff gun and carriage from above showing the 5 ton counter-weight in the raised position.*

Plate 47a-f: *Illustrations of shot, shell, cartridge and fiction tube used in the 110-pounder rifled breech loader on the Moncrieff carriage.*

SEGMENT SHELL

FRICTION TUBE

CARTRIDGE WITH COPPER LUBRICATOR

PART FOUR

SIDE-ARMS

Side-arms in artillery are the implements and tools which belong with each gun and carriage and are as follows:

BLOCKED-UP CARRIAGE AND MUZZLE LOADING GUN OF 1811.

1 Long rammer for pressing home the charge in the bore of the gun.

1 Long sponge for washing out the bore of the gun between each discharge.

2 Lever handspikes for levering the carriage in required direction. Also for fast elevation of the breech of the gun for range etc.

2 Roller handspikes applied to the rear of the carriage to run the carriage up and back.

1 Long worm for removing burnt debris in bore.

1 Vent pick for piercing the cartridge through the vent of the gun at the breech (**Plates 48 and 49**).

CASEMENT CARRIAGE FOR THE 110 POUNDER ARMSTRONG BREECH LOADER

2 Roller handspikes for running the gun and carriage up and back.

1 Short rammer for loading the shell and cartridge into the breech of the gun.

1 Long sponge for washing out the bore of the gun between each discharge.

2 Handspikes for levering the carriage in the required traversing direction.

MONCRIEFF DEPRESSION CARRIAGE FOR THE 110 POUNDER ARMSTRONG BREECH LOADER

1 Short rammer for loading the shell and cartridge into the breech of the gun.

1 Long sponge for washing out the bore of the gun between each discharge.

Plate 48: *The blocked-up carriage and 32 pounder cast-iron gun of 1811 Blomefield type on its C pivot, the muzzle of the gun depressed for loading, showing some of the side-arms.*

GUNS AND CARRIAGES

2 Round wooden metal shod handspikes to fit the round drum capstans for hauling up or down by hand the main elevator carriage and gun.

2 Wooden handspikes iron shod for traversing the main carriage platform on its sweep-plates.

SBBLs: Smooth Bored Breech Loaders
32 Pounders for the Caponier North
for each Gun and Carriage

1 Short rammer for loading the canister shot and cartridge

1 Long sponge for washing out the bore between discharges

2 Wooden handspikes for traversing the gun and carriage in the required direction.

Ranges

64 pounder of 64 cwt R.M.L. – 4000 yards

7-inch110 pounder of 82 cwt R.B.L. – 3600 yards

32 pounder S.B.B.L. – Close Range Case-Shot

25 pounder of 18 cwt R.M.L. – 4000 yards

32 pounder smooth bore M.L. – 2620 yards

Dates on which new guns and carriages
were set up at Crownhill Fort

Wooden blocked up traversing siege carriage:
    Delivered 29.7.97
    Set up 16.8.97

Wooden casemate traversing siege carriage and 110-pounder RBL of 82 cwt:
    Delivered and set up 29.10.97

Moncrieff depression carriage and 110-pounder RBL of 82 cwt:
    Delivered and set up 23-25.2.98

Four iron traversing carriages and four 32-pounder SBBLs
    Delivered 14.4.98
    Set up 23-24.4.98

Plate 49: *Re-enactment group of the 2nd Battery, 7th Western Brigade, Royal Garrison Artillery, after firing the 32-pounder muzzle loading gun on its blocked up traversing carriage. Left to right: Michael Davis, Christopher Bailey, Colin Wetton, John Symons, Shaun McCoy, Donald Day, Richard Eva and James Breslin.*

PART FIVE

A LIFE IN GUNS

The following are projects past and present in which the author has been personally involved concerning the display of historic artillery, culminating in 1998 with the export to Jamestown, Virginia, USA, of brass and iron guns and their carriages.

DARTMOUTH CASTLE OLD BATTERY, DEVON

In the early 1960s, after the completion of major renovations to the internal fabric of Dartmouth Castle in Devon, consideration was given to the two period pieces of heavy ordnance which had lain at the Old Battery adjacent to the Castle below the car park.

The battery had been rebuilt in the 1860s and the two smooth-bored guns of the 1840s had been replaced with rifled pieces. These were smooth-bored guns converted to three-groove rifled guns firing a 64 pound shot or shell known as Palliser conversion. These were named after the officer who first proposed the idea of utilising the best of the old smooth-bored cast-iron guns to the rifled system.

Being approached by the then Ministry of Works to display the guns in their original emplacement within the Old Battery~at least one carriage was needed. Old postcards of the 1880s depicted the battery with two casemate type wooden slides carrying carriages and guns mounted on the upper platform firing over or through a crenellation.

To gain authenticity it was decided to copy one of four original traversing siege carriages from the ramparts of the Royal Citadel in Plymouth and mount it *en barbette* in its original emplacement. The present carriage and slide you see today was built by two joiners, Albert Turrell and Gerald Widdicombe, just outside the old original 15th century rampart walls above the car park in a workshop which, at the time, was used as a site base for work to the Castle.

The two guns which had lain within the casemate for the last forty years or more were brought out and cleaned and painted. They originally started life as smooth bored guns cast at Woolwich Arsenal in about 1834 and identified as Millar pattern of 70 cwt, later to be converted.

GUNS AND CARRIAGES

The firm of Fox & Haggart Engineers, Vauxhall Street, Plymouth were contracted to install the carriage and mount the gun which entailed the lifting of gun and carriage over various walls, this was overseen by Desmond Northcott, Haggart's foreman. This all took place in 1963.

Since that date the firing of this piece for public display has taken place on numerous occasions by the Portsdown Volunteer Artillery.

This to my knowledge was the first coastal defence traversing siege carriage built since they were last produced by the War Department between 1885–1890s, and used by the then Artillery Volunteer Unit for various competition shoots.

PEVENSEY CASTLE, SUSSEX
THE DEMI-CULVERINE

There exists an old photograph of about 1890 showing the outer bailey of Pevensey Castle, Sussex, which depicts a cast-iron gun lying on two stone blocks.

This gun, it would appear, was delivered to Pevensey around 1547 along with another piece of the same type and design, which was removed from Pevensey Castle to the Woolwich Rotunda in 1865. It is possible that both guns came from William Lovet's Foundry in the county of Sussex.

Visitors to this ancient castle will see that the first mentioned piece is displayed mounted on a field or travelling carriage of a design in keeping with the heavy field or travelling carriages of the mid-16th century. The drawings for this carriage were prepared by the author in 1964.

BERMUDA AND PEMBROKE DOCK, SOUTH WALES

Two carriages built under the author's supervision. The first was the cast-iron slide and carriage to take a heavy muzzle loading 68-pounder cast-iron gun of 95 cwt, No. 693 by W & Co, 1858, of Dundas Pattern of 1848. This is now set up in the keep on Ireland Island, Bermuda, supporting various historic prints depicting carriages and guns of this type within the Bermuda Keep confines.

The second carriage and slide of this type (cast-iron) was produced in 1995 for the vacant emplacement atop the Victorian Martello type tower within Pembroke Dock, South Wales. This reproduction cast-iron slide and carriage was built to take an old original 18-pounder cast-iron smooth bored muzzle-loading gun of Blomefield type of the early 19th century (**Plate 50**).

JAMESTOWN AND YORKTOWN, USA

Further away from home, to the United States and the State of Virginia, a request came from Mr Eric Speth of the Jamestown Festival Park to produce

Plate 50: *An original 18-pounder Blomefield gun on a reproduction cast-iron carriage and traversing platform can be seen on the Martello Tower at Pembroke Dock, South Wales.*

Plate 51: *A brass light field gun and carriage, one of the mid 18th century reproduction guns sent to Yorktown, Virginia, USA.*

Plate 52: *A new field carriage built in 1996 with an original early 16th century bronze saker. Now on display at the National Army Museum, Chelsea, London.*

eight cast-iron falcons for the reproduction 17th century ship, the *Susan Constant*. Following that project the Yorktown Colonial Williamsburg organisation required a 6-pounder brass field piece for display purposes. Documentation records such guns and carriages were part of the British army ordnance used during the War of Independence (**Plate 51**).

ARMY MUSEUM, CHELSEA, LONDON

A project in 1996 involved the building of a field carriage to take and display a fine early 16th century saker, a 6-pounder. The property of the National Army Museum in London, this bronze gun had been in store for a number of years and deserved a carriage for display, along with the relevant side-arms for working and firing the piece. This is now displayed at their Army Museum at Chelsea, London (**Plate 52**).

CAWSAND BATTERY, EAST CORNWALL

To mark the occasion on which the Franco-Spanish Fleet anchored in Cawsand Bay in 1779, at the site of the Cawsand Bulwark in the vicinity of the now privately developed Cawsand Battery, two reproduction early 19th century cast-iron 24-pounder Blomefield pattern guns, with cast-iron open framed garrison carriages, were built and set up to the left and right of the war memorial (**Plate 53**).

HM NAVAL BASE, CAMELS HEAD, PLYMOUTH

Period cast-iron muzzle loading guns continue to be brought back either to demonstrate their original function or to stand as ornaments of past history. Two such guns can be seen at the entrance to Camels Head Gate, Plymouth naval establishment. Like many over the past thirty years they were excavated from their role as bollards within the network of roads throughout South Yard Naval Dockyard.

FORT GEORGE, SCOTLAND

In the 1970s a rare cast-iron muzzle loading gun was purchased from a scrap yard in the small town of Biggar, Lanarkshire, Scotland. As Historic Scotland had, at Fort George, an emplacement for a traversing wooden siege carriage of the dwarf pattern it was decided this would be an ideal site to take this gun. The piece was identified as a Mark 1 64-pounder of 64 cwt rifled muzzle loading gun and was the first type of rifled muzzle-loader. Accepted by the then War Department, this Mark I type can always be identified by its retention of the type of muzzle used on all previous Blomefield smooth bored cast-iron guns of the late 18th – early 19th century. This piece to my knowledge is possibly the sole surviving Mark 1 in the British Isles. It was introduced into service in 1864 when it was intended to replace the 7-inch RBL in the navy.

Plate 53: *The war memorial above Cawsand, Cornwall, with two cast-iron 24-pounder reproduction 19th century guns and carriages. The author, left, and James Breslin, the project officer, right, who researched the background data to the Old Cawsand Bulwark for the Groundwork Trust, Plymouth.*

Throughout the south west there are numerous sites displaying cannon, some of which are open to the public. For those interested, the following locations are given in addition to sites already noted.

ROYAL CITADEL, PLYMOUTH

The Royal Citadel, Plymouth, holds an interesting number of muzzle loading guns ranging from brass field pieces of 1809, cast-iron converted guns, and rifled pieces of the 1870-1880. Three of these examples are mounted on original coastal defence wooden traversing siege carriages. There were originally four until one was removed by Royal Armouries and sent to Fort Nelson to enhance their own collection. Among these historic pieces is a regimental gun, a brass licorne (Russian), cast in Briansk, and captured at the Crimean War of 1854–56, at the Battle of Alma. There are also two iron 10-inch mortars of British origin on original cast-iron beds.

ARMADA MONUMENT, PLYMOUTH HOE

Close to the Royal Citadel on Plymouth Hoe is the Armada Monument with a statue of Sir Francis Drake. At the base of this monument is a brass gun, a 3 pounder, of Danish origin. It is the class and type of cannon that was usually cast with lifting handles of dolphin shape (as they are sometimes called), but in this case these lifting handles are in the form of elephant heads with their trunks forming the loops. The monogram on this piece is of King Frederick V of Denmark, dated 1757. The main pedestal also displays two mortars in cast-iron with 8-inch bores and cast-iron beds, both of English manufacture. One is marked on its left trunnion 'No. 32', the right trunnion 'B.P. & Co' for Bailey Pegg & Co of Wapping, Bankside, London (1812–1966). The date of casting is approximately 1850–60.

LUNDY ISLAND

Little known, two original guns and carriages can be seen on the Island of Lundy, off the North Devon coast. They were originally sent there to be used for fog signals, to warn shipping in bad weather. They are 18-pounder cast-iron Blomefield guns of 1810 vintage on original carriages of the 1830–40s. Their condition is somewhat distressed and they urgently require shot-blasting and painting before their condition deteriorates beyond conservation.

This island, owned by the National Trust, is administered by the Landmark Trust, who will, in time, no doubt apply their expertise to their conservation.

CROWNHILL FORT MORTARS

The impressive entrance to Crownhill Fort displayed, for approximately twenty years, two 8-inch cast-iron mid-Victorian mortars. These pieces are both marked on their right trunnions with the letter 'S' denoting the foundry which produced them, Sturges & Co of Bradford, Yorkshire. They set up their company in 1788 and supplied guns, especially mortars, to the Board of Ordnance between 1790-1820. The company and foundry were known as the Bowling Iron Works and guns and mortars can still be found bearing the word 'Bowling' and the letter 'S'.

GUNS AND CARRIAGES

This pair of mortars was at one time set up outside Cumberland Barracks, Plymouth, before their transfer to Crownhill Fort. They are still in Plymouth and can be seen at Mount Wise naval establishment. They also spent some time at Seaton Barracks.

The iron beds which support these pieces do not belong with these mortars, being made for mortars of a larger calibre.

CROWNHILL FORT CARRONADE

A small piece of muzzle-loading artillery, which can be seen accompanying the smooth bored breech-loading guns in the main north caponier, is a carronade produced by the foundry of Bailey Pegg & Co, 1812–1966, who specialised in the production of carronades for the merchant service and various trading posts throughout the world. The bore is 3-inch with the breech marked 'B.P. & Co' below a crown. Its carriage is a blocked-trail type in wood with cast-iron trucks for garrison use. This piece was originally the property of Major Thomas Hitchins.

CROWNHILL FORT SWIVEL GUN

A type of ordnance built by the author in the 1970s, which has found a home in Crownhill Fort, is the hand-forged wrought iron breech-loading swivel gun with a bore diameter of 1.5-inches. It was built to research the range and accuracy of a late 15th century swivel gun. These were mainly used from the rails of ancient wooden men of war and were prolific from the mid 15th century to the early 18th century in all seafaring nations.

CROWNHILL FORT GUARDROOM

Here is a small cast-iron muzzle loading gun of the mid to late 18th century. It is interesting in that at least four of this type have been recorded around the Plymouth area, and two identical guns are owned by the author. No doubt there are others in the West Country from the same foundry. Its bore is 2-inch and it would have fired solid shot or grape shot up to ranges of 300-400 yards. The piece is marked 2-2-25 (2 cwt, 2 qtrs, 25 lbs).

Crownhill Fort and its establishment have been most successful in presenting this fortification to the general public, and will no doubt continue to make further improvements, such as the mounting of other pieces of period ordnance which we know once existed in their purpose-built emplacements around the ramparts.

The museum displays and educational facilities have made this Palmerston fortification, the largest of Plymouth's Victorian forts, a jewel in the crown of period military sites in Britain.

Plate 54: *The author with a new field carriage under construction for Jamestown Festival Park, USA. The carriage was built to take a reproduction cast-iron gun of early 17th century type.*

APPENDIX A

Projects concerning the casting of cannon, construction of carriages, repairs, and the siting of period and reproduction ordnance over the past thirty-five years, as supervised by the author:

1963 Dartmouth Castle, Devon

Wooden traversing siege carriage.

1964 Pevensey Castle, Sussex

Wooden field carriage.

1966 Waterlooville, Hampshire

Wooden garrison carriage.

1966 Caernarvon Castle, North Wales

Wooden garrison carriage.

1968 Yarmouth Castle, Isle of Wight

Wooden sea service carriage

1970 Dartmouth Castle, Devon

Six wooden garrison carriages.

1971 Tilbury Fort, Essex

Wooden garrison carriage.

1971 Royal Citadel, Plymouth, Devon

Wooden garrison carriage and repair to original wooden traversing siege carriages.

1971 Pendennis Castle, Falmouth, Cornwall

Ten wooden garrison carriages.

1971 St Mawes Castle, Cornwall

Two wooden garrison carnages.

1971   Cromwell's Castle, Tresco, Isles of Scilly

Two wooden garrison carriages.

1972   Royal Citadel, Plymouth, Devon

Repairs to wooden field carriage.

GUNS AND CARRIAGES

1972   Tilbury Fort, Essex

Three wooden field carriages.

1972   St Mawes Castle, Cornwall

Two wooden sea service carriages.

1972   Fort Brockhurst, Gosport, Hampshire

Repairs to Japanese howitzer and carriage.

1972   St Mary's, Isles of Scilly

Three wooden garrison carriages.

1972   Pevensey Castle, Sussex

Repairs to wheel of field carriage.

1973   St Mary's, Isles of Scilly

Wooden field carriage.

1973   Fort Brockhurst, Hampshire

Three block trail carriages for carronades.

1973 Berwick-upon-Tweed, Northumberland

Wooden field carriage.

1974 Royal Citadel, Plymouth, Devon

Repairs to wheels of field carriage.

1974 Fort Brockhurst, Gosport, Hampshire

Refurbishment of nine ships' carriages.

1974 St Mawes Castle, Cornwall

Wooden garrison carriage.

1975 Mountbatten Tower, Plymouth, Devon

Three wooden sea service carriages.

1975 Yarmouth Castle, Isle of Wight

Wooden traversing siege carriage.

1975 Royal Citadel, Plymouth, Devon

Repairs to garrison carriage.

1975 Tower of London

Wooden block trail carriage for carronade.

GUNS AND CARRIAGES

Repairs to five wooden garrison carriages.

Two Napoleonic field carriages.

1976 Pendennis Castle, Falmouth, Cornwall

Wooden traversing siege carriage and wooden garrison carriage.

1976 St Mary's, Isles of Scilly

Wooden garrison carriage.

1976 Fort Brockhurst, Hampshire

Wooden traversing siege carriage

1977 Fort George, Nr Inverness, Scotland

Wooden traversing siege carriage.

1977 Royal Artillery Institution, Woolwich Rotunda, London

Wooden field carriage

1977 Royal Citadel, Plymouth, Devon

Wooden sea service carriage.

Repairs to wooden garrison carriages.

1977 Tower of London

Repairs to field carriage.

1977 Berwick-upon-Tweed, Northumberland

Twelve wooden garrison carriages.

1978 Portland Castle, Dorset

Four wooden garrison carriages.

1978 Pendennis Castle, Falmouth, Cornwall

Two wooden block trail carriages for carronades

1979 St Mawes Castle, Cornwall

Two wooden sea service carriages.

1980 Pendennis Castle, Falmouth, Cornwall

Seven cast-iron sakers and seven wooden base-board carriages

1983 Drake's Island, Plymouth, Devon

Steel traversing siege carriage for 12-inch 25 ton RML.

1984 Tower of London

GUNS AND CARRIAGES

Repairs to seven wooden field carriages.

1985   Calshot Castle, Hampshire

Three wooden sea service carriages and three cast-iron garrison carriages.

1985   St Mawes Castle, Cornwall

Wooden field carriage for Alberghetti.

1985   Bermuda Maritime Museum, Bermuda

Seven cast-iron garrison carriages.

1985 Castle Cornet, Guernsey, Channel Islands

Wooden truck carriage for falcon.

1986 Dover Castle, Kent

Five wooden garrison carriages.

Four cast-iron garrison carriages.

1986   Hurst Castle, Hampshire

Steel traversing siege carriage for 12.5-inch 38 ton RML.

1986   Powys Castle, Welshpool, Powys, Wales

Restoration of two Indian wooden field carriages of Tipoo Sahib.

1986   Fort Nelson, Fareham, Hampshire

Seven new breech blocks for 32 pounder S.B.B.Ls.

1986 Castle Cornet, Guernsey, Channel Islands

Seven cast-iron sakers.

1986   Plymouth, Massachusetts, USA

Cast-iron saker.

Wooden garrison carriage.

1987 Williamsburg, Virginia, USA

Two cast-iron sakers.

1987 Jamestown, Virginia, USA

Three cast-iron sakers.

1987   Royal Citadel, Plymouth, Devon

Wooden field carriage for Gribeauval.

1988   St Mawes Castle, Cornwall

GUNS AND CARRIAGES

Two wooden garrison carriages.

1988   Tilbury Fort, Essex
Repairs to two wooden garrison carriages.

1988   Pendennis Castle, Falmouth, Cornwall

Replica Pevensey gun, field carriage and limber.

1988   Hurst Castle, Hampshire

Two wooden garrison carriages.

Assembly of twin 6 pounder.

1988   Gun Powder Mills, Postbridge, Devon

Mortar bed for 8-inch cast-iron mortar.

1988 Nassau, The Bahamas

Two cast-iron 9 pounder guns.

1988   Fort Nelson, Fareham, Hampshire

Two wooden garrison carriages.

Steel field carriage.

1989 Portland Castle, Dorset

Wooden garrison carriage.

1989   St Mary's, Isles of Scilly

Two cast-iron garrison carriages.

1989 St Mawes Castle, Cornwall

Wrought-iron swivel gun on a trestle.

1989 Pendennis Castle, Falmouth, Cornwall

Wrought-iron swivel gun on a trestle.

1989 Dartmouth Castle, Devon

Wrought-iron bedstock gun.

1989 Fort Nelson, Fareham, Hampshire

Two wooden field carriages.

Restoration of 7-inch of 72 cwt R.BL.

1989   Bermuda Maritime Museum, Bermuda

 Cast-iron saker and wooden sea service carriage.

1990 Dartmouth Castle, Devon

GUNS AND CARRIAGES

Wooden traversing siege carriage.

Two wooden garrison carriages.

Wooden block trail carriage for carronade.

1990   Royal Citadel, Plymouth, Devon

Wooden traversing siege carriage.

1990 Hurst Castle, Hampshire

Repairs to 12 pounder, QF gun.

Wooden garrison carriage.

Steel traversing siege carriage for second 12.5-inch 38 ton RML.

1990 Upnor Castle, Kent

Wooden garrison carriage.

Repairs to two wooden garrison carriages.

1990 Redan Hill, Aldershot, Hampshire

Cast-iron 32 pounder gun and cast-iron garrison carriage.

1990 Bermuda Maritime Museum, Bermuda

Two cast-iron sakers.

Two wooden truck carriages.

Wooden block trail field carriage for 40 pounder RBL.

1990   Tantallon Castle, East Lothian, Scotland

Wrought-iron bedstock gun.

1991 Tilbury Fort, Essex

Overhauling 12-pounder QF gun.

1991 Fort Nelson, Fareham, Hampshire

Wrought-iron bedstock gun.

1992 Portland Castle, Dorset

Wooden sea service carriage.

1992 St Mary's, Isles of Scilly

Two cast-iron garrison carriages. and two wooden garrison carriages.

Wooden traversing siege carriage to Rutherford's design.

GUNS AND CARRIAGES

1992 Hampshire County Museum Service, Winchester, Hampshire

Cast-iron saker.

1992 Bermuda Maritime Museum, Bermuda

Cast-iron traversing carriage for 68-pounder 95 cwt.

1992 Jamestown, Virginia, USA

Two wrought-iron swivel guns.

Eight cast-iron falcons.

Eight wooden ship's carriages.

1993 HM Naval Base, Camels Head Gate, Plymouth Devon

Two cast-iron garrison carriages

1993 Pendennis Castle, Falmouth, Cornwall

Cast-iron saker.

Wooden early 17th century Vauban type fortress carriage.

1993 St Mary's, Isles of Scilly

Wooden garrison carriage.

1993 Jamestown, Virginia, USA

Two cast-iron falcons.

Two wooden ship's carriages.

1994 Dover Castle, Kent

Wooden mortar bed for 1684 cast-iron mortar.

1994 Pendennis Castle, Falmouth, Cornwall

Wooden garrison carriage.

Repairs to 12 pounder QF gun and 4.7-inch QF gun.

1994 Royal Citadel, Plymouth, Devon

Repairs to wooden traversing siege carriages and wooden garrison carriages.

1994 Nassau, The Bahamas

Two wooden garrison carriages for 9 pounders.

1994 Bermuda Maritime Museum, Bermuda

Bronze open frame garrison carriage.

GUNS AND CARRIAGES

1994 Yorktown, Virginia, USA

Two brass light 6-pounders.

Wooden field carriage.

1994 Rousse Tower, Guernsey, Channel Islands

Six cast-iron guns.

Five cast-iron garrison carriages.

1994 Jamestown, Virginia, USA

Two cast-iron falcons.

Two wooden ship's carriages.

1994 Craigievar Castle, Aberdeenshire, Scotland

Two wooden garrison carriages.

1995 Pendennis Castle, Falmouth, Cornwall

Repairs to 6-inch BL gun.

1995 Gun Tower, Pembroke Dock, South Wales

Cast-iron traversing carriage

1995 Windsor Castle, Berkshire

Repairs to wooden garrison carriage.

1996 Osborne House, Isle of Wight

Two wooden ship's carriages.

1996   Cawsand Bulwark, East Cornwall

Two cast-iron 24 pounder guns.

Two cast-iron garrison carriages.

1996 Rotherham, Yorkshire

Wooden sea service carriage.

1996 Windsor Castle, Berkshire

Repairs to wooden Lutine carriage.

1996 National Army Museum, Chelsea, London

Wooden field carriage.

1996 Guernsey Tourist Board, Guernsey, Channel Islands

Wooden block trail carriage for carronade.

GUNS AND CARRIAGES

Plate 55: *One of three bronze swivel guns, comprising barrel, swivel and four chamber pots, awaiting machining.*

1996 Brodick Castle, Isle of Arran, Scotland

Brass gun and wooden truck carriage.

1997 Westman Island, Iceland

Brass light 6 pounder.

1997–1998 Crownhill Fort, Plymouth, Devon

Two 110 pounder 82 cwt BL guns

Moncrieff counter-weight carriage.

Wooden blocked-up traversing siege carriage.

Wooden casemate traversing siege carriage.

Four cast-iron 32 pounder SBBLs.

Four steel traversing carriages for SBBLs.

1998 Dover Castle, Kent

Two wooden block trail carriages for carronades.

1998 Bermuda Maritime Museum, Bermuda

Three wooden sea service carriages.

1998 Jamestown, Virginia, USA

Three brass breech loading swivel guns.

Cast-iron saker and wooden field carriage. (**Plates 54, 55, 56, 57 and 58**).

81

Plate 56: *Reproduction early 17th century bronze breech loading swivel gun under proof firing. One of three such guns made for Jamestown, Virginia, USA.*

Plate 57: *The completed field carriage ready for delivery to Jamestown, USA.*

Plate 58: *The author test firing the Jamestown gun before dispatch to the USA.*

APPENDIX B

In the course of his work on the restoration and reproduction of guns and carriages the author has constantly referred to many original prints and working drawings, both those in official archives and in private hands. His own collection of historic photographs is considerable and a few rare and relevant samples are included here

Plate 59: *Cast iron French Napoleonic guns on cast iron garrison carriages at Garden Battery, Mount Edgcumbe, Cornwall, c. 1870. Lead covers are set across the touch-holes at the breech of each gun to protect the bores. There were seventeen pieces in all which were used for saluting purposes. Only three of the guns remain today.*

Plate 60: *The Royal Citadel, Plymouth, February 1856. This photograph, possibly taken by William Henry Fox Talbot, shows a cast iron howitzer on a rear-chock carriage, with a garland of shot or shell. Captain Stafford Baxter is seen next to the gun.*

Plate 61: *Carisbrook Castle, Isle of Wight, c. 1880. Two detachments training on smooth bore 32-pounder Blomefield guns on traversing platforms. The site still exists.*

Plate 62: *The Plympton Volunteers, Devon, in 1897, with what appear to be Millar pattern guns. Note the Millar pattern sight set up on the mid section of the gun in the foreground.*

Plate 63: *A battery of muzzle loading guns with shot piles and magazines on Gibraltar, 1880.*

Plate 64: *A view of the battery in the Citadel, Quebec, Canada in 1880. The guns, on cast iron carriages and slides, are English smooth bore guns converted to rifled pieces on the Palliser system. Note the substitute wooden blocks in place of the rear carriage trucks to restrict recoil, and the piles of Palliser shells to the rear.*

GUNS AND CARRIAGES

Plate 65: *Summer camp at Arbroath, Scotland, c. 1890. The guns are Palliser type, possibly Millar or Dundas pattern 64-pounder RMLs.*

91

Plate 66: *Armstrong Mark 1 9-inch of 12 tons RMLs of 1865, removed from the casemates on Drake's Island in Plymouth Sound before the First World War. After lying on the rocks for many years they were shipped to Millbay Docks to be cut up for scrap in 1940. Originally introduced as broadside guns for ironclad ships, and for the defence of harbours and seafronts, 190 were made.*

Plate 67: *Repository drill on a 7-inch 110-pounder breech loading gun on a traversing siege carriage. A photograph taken in 1861.*

Plate 68: *An Armstrong 40-pounder rifled breech loader of 1860 on its original carriage. This gun was set up in Eastern Road Ashburton, Devon, in 1904 at the end of the Boer War, by Lieutenant-General Sir Charles Tucker, Retired, of The Hall, Ashburton.*

Plate 69: *Chalmers Casemate, built of masonry at Shoeburyness Proof Establishment. The casemate was destroyed by gunfire to test the velocity and penetration of a variety of guns and projectiles. This photograph records an experiment undertaken by the Ordnance Select Committee in 1861.*

GLOSSARY

ARMSTRONG: Sir William Armstrong, appointed Engineer of Rifled Ordnance and Superintendent of the Royal Gun Factory in 1859.

BLOCKED-UP: A Traversing Siege Carriage built for a 6 ft. Parapet to cover the Glacis.

BLOMEFIELD: Major General Sir Thomas Blomefield, Inspector of Artillery and Inspector of the Royal Brass Foundry 1780-1822.

CAPONIER: Underground casemate projecting into a ditch to provide flanking fire.

CARRON: Carron Company, Falkirk, Scotland 1759-1982.

CASEMATE: An enclosed gun emplacement for a gun firing through a loop, hole or embrasure in an outer wall.

C PIVOT: There were six different types of pivot mounting in emplacements for traversing, lettered A–F. The C Pivot mounting was centred in a 360° racer.

ELEVATOR: The main carriage which carries the 7 inch RBL and works on the Moncrieff platform.

EMPLACEMENT: Area within a fort to house various types of guns and carriages.

FLANGE: A casting which carries a wheel or roller.

FRICTION TUBE: A hollow metal tube partially filled with priming powder and a small charge of fulminate of mercury, ignited by a rasp set in the fulminate and pulled by a lanyard.

HANDSPIKES: Long wooden levers used for moving and jacking a gun carriage for laying the piece.

HAXO CASEMATE: A vaulted casemate on the terreplein providing overhead cover for gun and detachment, named after its inventor General F.B. Haxo 1774-1838.

MILLAR: General William Millar, Inspector General at Woolwich Arsenal 1827-1838 designed Millar Pattern Sights for heavy guns.

GUNS AND CARRIAGES

MONCRIEFF PIT: Type of emplacement which housed a Moncrieff depression carriage and protected the gun detachment below a 9ft parapet.

PALMERSTON: Lord Palmerston, throughout his years as Prime Minister, perceiving the threat of invasion from the French, instigated the building of forts around the coast.

RACERS: Iron rails on which a gun traverses.

RBL: Rifled breech loader.

SBBL: Smooth bored breech loader used in caponiers for the defence of ditches and flanks, these were converted from 32-pounder muzzle loading guns.

SWEEP PLATES: Traversing plates with cross-hatching for the insertion of iron-shod wooden handspikes for traversing the Moncrieff depression carriage.

VENT: Small hole drilled at the breech of a gun to take the friction tube to fire the main charge.

WD: War Department, now the Ministry of Defence.

FURTHER READING

CAMPBELL, R.H. *Carron Company*. Oliver & Boyd, Edinburgh and London, 1961.

CARPENTER, A.C. *Cannon, the Conservation, Reconstruction and Presentation of Historic Artillery*. Halsgrove, 1993.

DOUGAN, D. *The Great Gunmaker, The Story of Lord Armstrong*. Frank Graham, Newcastle-upon-Tyne, 1970.

GRIFFITHS, Captain F.A. *The Artillerist's Manual and British Soldier's Compendium*. E. Jones, Woolwich, 1847.

Handbooks for the 7 inch Rifled Breech Loading Guns of 72 cwt. and 82 cwt. on Moncrieff and Sliding Carriages. H.M.S.O. 1885 and 1897.

Handbooks for the 32 pr. S.B.B.L. Gun for Flank Defence. H.M.S.O. 1885 and 1898.

HOGG, I.V. *Coast Defences of England and Wales, 1856-1956*. David & Charles, Newton Abbot., 1974.

MAURICE-JONES, K.W. *The History of Coast Artillery in the British Army*. Royal Artillery Institution, London, 1959.

MOORE, D. *Crownhill Fort, Plymouth*. Plymouth Papers No.1. David Moore, 1994.

MOORE, D. *The Moncrieff Story*. Palmerston Forts Society, 1992 & 1995.

PYE, A. & WOODWARD, F. *The Historic Defences of Plymouth*. Cornwall County Council, 1996

REID, W. *Arms Through the Ages*. Harper & Row, U.S.A., 1976.

Treatise on Military Carriages. H.M.S.O., 1879 and 1888.

WOODWARD, F. *Forts or Follies? A History of Plymouth's Palmerston Forts*. Halsgrove, 1998.

WOODWARD, F.W. *Plymouth's Defences*. F.W. Woodward, 1990.

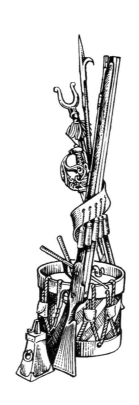

INDEX

GUNS AND CARRIAGES